Eb Alto Saxophone—Book 2 **SECOND EDITION**

Tradition of Excellence™

Comprehensive Band Method

by Bruce Pearson & Ryan Nowlin

Dear Student:

Congratulations! You have successfully attained the first level of excellence in music-making. By now, you have discovered that careful study and regular practice have brought you the joy and satisfaction of making beautiful music. You are now ready to move to the next level. We want to welcome you to *Tradition of Excellence*, Book 2, and wish you continued success and enjoyment!

Bruce Pearson   Bruce Pearson

Ryan Nowlin   Ryan Nowlin

PRACTICE JOURNAL

Week	Date Assigned	Assignment/Goal	Minutes Practiced							Total Minutes	Initial
			Su	M	Tu	W	Th	F	Sa		
1											
2											
3											
4											
5											
6											
7											
8											
9											
10											
11											
12											
13											
14											
15											
16											

A full Practice Journal is available from your teacher or from your **INTERACTIVE Practice Studio**.

 Enhance your practice by frequently visiting the **INTERACTIVE Practice Studio**. See the inside back cover for more information.

 *Tradition of Excellence* is available in SmartMusic. To subscribe, go to www.smartmusic.com.

ISBN 10: 0-8497-7131-5 • ISBN 13: 978-0-8497-7131-6

©2011, 2016 Kjos Music Press, Neil A. Kjos Music Company, Distributor, 4382 Jutland Drive, San Diego, California, 92117.
International copyright secured. All rights reserved. Printed in U.S.A.

 Tradition of Excellence and **INTERACTIVE Practice Studio** are trademarks of Kjos Music Press.

Theory & Composition

I – Roman numeral used to identify a tonic chord

IV – Roman numeral used to identify a subdominant chord

V⁷ – Roman numeral and number 7 used to identify a dominant seventh chord

orchestration – choice of instruments used to play the music

whole step – interval consisting of two half steps

major scale – series of whole (w) and half (h) steps in the following pattern: 1 2 3 4 5 6 7 8
w w h w w w h

arpeggio – notes of a chord sounded one after another

Notes

1. Warm-up: Chop Builder

2. Academic Festival March — *Duet*

Brahms wrote this piece in 1880 for the University of Breslau for awarding him an honorary degree.

Johannes Brahms (1833–1897)
German Composer

3. Split Decision

orchestration

4. Arroró Mi Niño

▶ Orchestrate by writing in the instruments that will play each time.

Argentinian Folk Song

1st x _____

2nd x _____

major scale, arpeggio, I, IV, V⁷

5. G Major Scale, Arpeggio, and Chords (Concert B♭ Major)

I   IV   I   V⁷   I

6. Skill Builder ✓ TEST

7. Alto Saxophone Private Lesson

▶ Use the alternate fingering on notes with *.

MASTERING EXCELLENCE: p. 40, #1

REVIEW

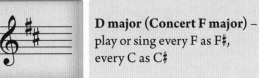

Key Signature

D major (Concert F major) – play or sing every F as F♯, every C as C♯

Notes

8. Warm-up: Tone Builder

Moderato

9. Ellacombe — *Duet*

German Hymn

▶ Circle the notes changed by the D major (Concert F major) key signature, highlighted in purple.

Moderato

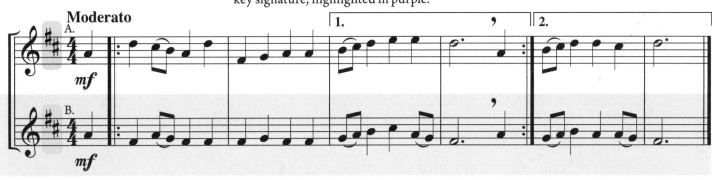

10. D Major Scale, Arpeggio, and Chords (Concert F Major)

Moderato

Major Scale   Arpeggio   Chords **div.**

I   IV   I   V⁷   I

11. *Sight-Reading Challenge:* Waves on the Sea

Irish Folk Song

Allegro

12. Skill Builder ✔ TEST

Moderato

13. Excellence in Theory

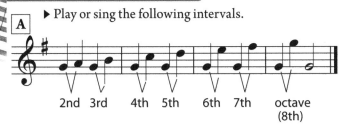

A ▶ Play or sing the following intervals.

2nd   3rd   4th   5th   6th   7th   octave (8th)

B ▶ Identify the following ascending intervals.

REVIEW

Terms & Symbols

Notes

14. Warm-up: Chop Builder

15. Chorale: Old Hundredth — *Band Arrangement*

Louis Bourgeois (c. 1510–1560)
French Composer

16. C Major Scale, Arpeggio, and Chords (Concert E♭ Major)

17. Report Card Blues

The blues developed in the United States during the early 1900s as an outgrowth of African-American spirituals and work songs. Blues melodies are usually 12 measures long.

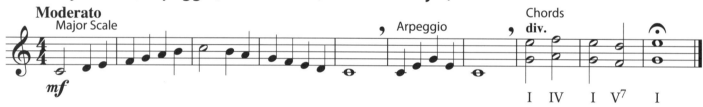

18. Skill Builder ✓ TEST

19. Alto Saxophone Private Lesson

W62XE

REVIEW

Rhythm

dotted quarter note = 1½ counts of sound in $\frac{2}{4}$, $\frac{3}{4}$, $\frac{4}{4}$, or 𝄴

COUNTING & CONDUCTING

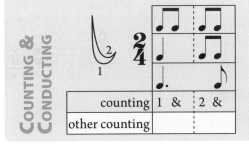

	counting	1	&	2	&
	other counting				

Terms & Symbols

Largo – very slow tempo

Da Capo al Fine (D.C. al Fine) – go back to the beginning of the piece and play or sing until the *Fine*

20. Wavelengths

Allegro

21. Dotted Quarters

▶ The bottom line provides the basic pulse.

Moderato

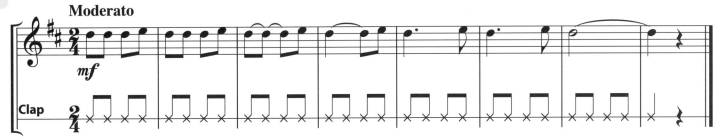

22. "Largo" from Symphony No. 9

Dvořák wrote this piece while on a tour of the United States. In addition to New York, he visited Spillville, Iowa, a town that had a large Czech population.

Antonín Dvořák (1841–1904)
Czech Composer

Largo

23. Skill Builder ✓ TEST

▶ Name the key of **23. Skill Builder.** _____

Andante

24. Excellence in Ear Training

▶ Write the melody of "My Country, 'Tis of Thee/God Save the Queen" in the staff provided. Several notes are written to help you.

Terms & Symbols

ritardando (***ritard.*** or ***rit.***) – gradually slow the tempo

Maestoso – majestically

25. Warm-up: Spanish Hymn

Traditional Spanish Hymn

26. Gentle Zephyr

ritardando

27. These Hallowed Halls — *Duet*

Maestoso

28. Regal Procession

29. Skill Builder ✓ TEST

30. Alto Saxophone Private Lesson

REVIEW

Rhythm

syncopation – rhythmic effect that places emphasis on a weak beat

Theory & Composition

transposition – taking a composition in one key and putting it into another

31. Leapfrog
Andante

32. Graceful Waltz
Allegro

33. New Horizon
Moderato

syncopation

34. Rhythm Time
▶ 1) Write the counting and clap the rhythm before you play. 2) Play on the note B (Concert D).

Moderato

RHYTHM STUDIES: p. 45, #2, 15

35. The Wabash Cannonball
American Folk Song

Moderato

36. Still, Still, Still ✓ TEST
▶ Add dynamics before you play.
Austrian Carol

Andante

37. Excellence in Theory
▶ Rewrite **25. Warm-up: Spanish Hymn** in the key of D major (Concert F major). Be sure to include the tempo and all the slurs and dynamics. Several notes are provided to guide your writing. Play your transposition.

Fine   *D.C. al Fine*

transposition

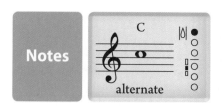

Notes

38. Warm-up: Chop Builder

39. *Sight-Reading Challenge:* My Heart's Tonight in Texas

American Folk Song

40. The Minstrel Boy — *Duet*

▸ Name the key of **40. The Minstrel Boy.** _____

Irish Folk Song

41. Skill Builder  TEST

42. Alto Saxophone Private Lesson

▸ Use the alternate fingering on notes with ∗ .

MASTERING EXCELLENCE: p. 40, #2

Key Signature

E minor (Concert G minor) – play or sing every F as F#

Terms & Symbols

courtesy accidental or **cautionary accidental** – reminder that the bar line has canceled an accidental

Theory & Composition

minor scale – series of whole (w) and half (h) steps in the following patterns:

natural minor: 1 2 3 4 5 6 7 8 — w h w w h w w

harmonic minor: 1 2 3 4 5 6 7 8 — w h w w h w+h h

melodic minor: 1 2 3 4 5 6 7 8 8 7 6 5 4 3 2 1 — w h w w w w h w w h w w w h

Lower case Roman numerals are used to indicate minor chords.
i – minor tonic chord in minor key
iv – minor subdominant chord in minor key
v – minor dominant chord in minor key
(the major dominant chord, V^7, is often used in minor keys)

Notes

---

43. E Natural Minor Scale, Arpeggio, and Chords (Concert G Minor)

i iv i v i

44. E Harmonic Minor Scale, Arpeggio, and Chords (Concert G Minor)

i iv i V^7 i

45. E Melodic Minor Scale, Arpeggio, and Chords (Concert G Minor)

i iv i V^7 i

46. Minka, Minka

▶ Which form of the minor scale is used in **46. Minka, Minka**? _____

Ukrainian Folk Song

Hey!

47. Coronado

48. Skill Builder ✓ TEST

▶ Also play with these articulations: A) B) C)

49. Excellence in Ear Training

▶ Listen to the following half steps and whole steps on the recorded accompaniments. If you hear a half step, circle H; if you hear a whole step, circle W.

a) **H W**   b) **H W**   c) **H W**   d) **H W**

ENSEMBLE

Theory & Composition

binary form – music with two different sections

Concert Etiquette

— Enter the stage or performance area confidently. Make eye contact with the audience and smile.

— Stand or sit tall. Be positive and energetic. It's fun to share your music with others!

Solo: A   **Duet:** A + B   **Trio** or **Full Band:** A + B + C

Ding Dong Merrily On High

French Carol

A December Triptych
(Adeste Fideles; Pat-a-Pan; Chanukah, O Chanukah)

Traditional Carols
arr. Ryan Nowlin (b. 1978)
American Composer

▸ Notice the key signature change at 24. ▸ Notice the tempo changes at 24 and 39.

W62XE

Rhythm

eighth rest = ½ count of silence in 2/4, 3/4, 4/4, or C ; an eighth rest is as long as an eighth note

Terms & Symbols

tenuto – sustain a note for its full value

Notes

50. Warm-up: Chorale — *Band Arrangement*

Joseph Barnby (1838–1896)
English Composer

Andante

51. Rhythm Time

▶ 1) Write the counting and clap the rhythm before you play. 2) Play on the note B (Concert D).

Moderato

RHYTHM STUDIES: p. 45, #3, 9, 16-18

52. Reuben and Rachel

▶ 1) Play both the black and gray notes to play the theme.
2) Replace each gray note with an eighth rest to create a variation.

American Folk Song

Moderato

53. Skill Builder: The Bridge at Avignon — *Duet*

French Folk Song

Allegro

54. El Capitan   ✓ TEST

This famous march is made up of themes from Sousa's operetta "El Capitan," which had its premiere on Broadway in 1896 and toured the country for the next four years.

John Philip Sousa (1854–1932)
American Composer

Allegro

55. Alto Saxophone Private Lesson

▶ Use the alternate fingering on notes with *.

MASTERING EXCELLENCE: p. 40, #3

Key Signature

F major (Concert A♭ major) – play or sing every B as B♭

Theory & Composition

G blues scale (Concert B♭ blues)

Notes

56. *Sight-Reading Challenge:* Minuet

Until recently, musicologists thought this piece was written by Johann Sebastian Bach.

Christian Petzold (c. 1677–1733)
German Composer

Moderato

57. El Encanto

Andante

58. F Major Scale, Arpeggio, and Chords (Concert A♭ Major)

Moderato
Major Scale   Arpeggio   Chords **div.**

I   IV   I   V⁷   I

59. Skill Builder

▶ Circle the notes changed by the key signature.

Moderato

60. Botany Bay ✓TEST

Australian Folk Song

Allegro

61. Excellence in Ear Training

▶ First, play the blues scale at the top of the page. Then, practice this exercise with the recorded accompaniment. Listen in measures 1, 3, 5, and 7. In measures 2, 4, 6, and 8, echo what you heard. Your starting notes are shown.

blues scale

Listen   Play   Listen   Play   Listen   Play   Listen   Play

62. Warm-up: Chop Builder

63. Theme from "Symphony No. 5"

Symphony No. 5 marked Beethoven's transition from the Classical to the Romantic Period.

Ludwig van Beethoven (1770–1827)
German Composer

64. Skill Builder

65. Rhythm Time

▶ 1) Write the counting and clap the rhythm before you play. 2) Play on the note B♭ (Concert D♭).

RHYTHM STUDIES: p. 45, #1, 7-8, 13-14

66. This Train ✓ TEST

▶ Orchestrate by writing in the instruments that will play each four-measure phrase.

American Spiritual

67. Alto Saxophone Private Lesson

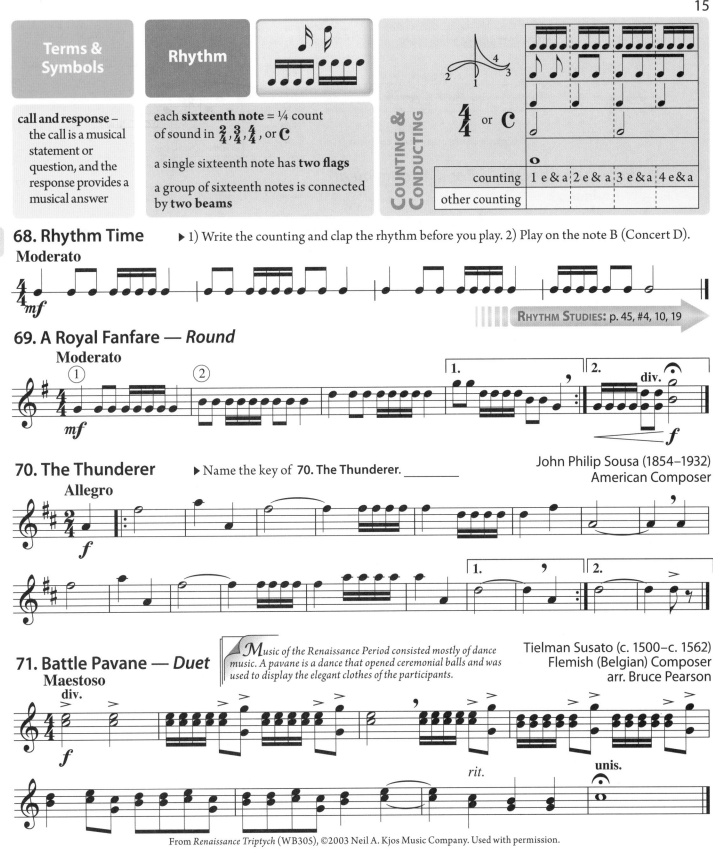

Rhythm

eighth/sixteenth note combination

COUNTING & CONDUCTING

	counting	1 e & a	2 e & a
	other counting		

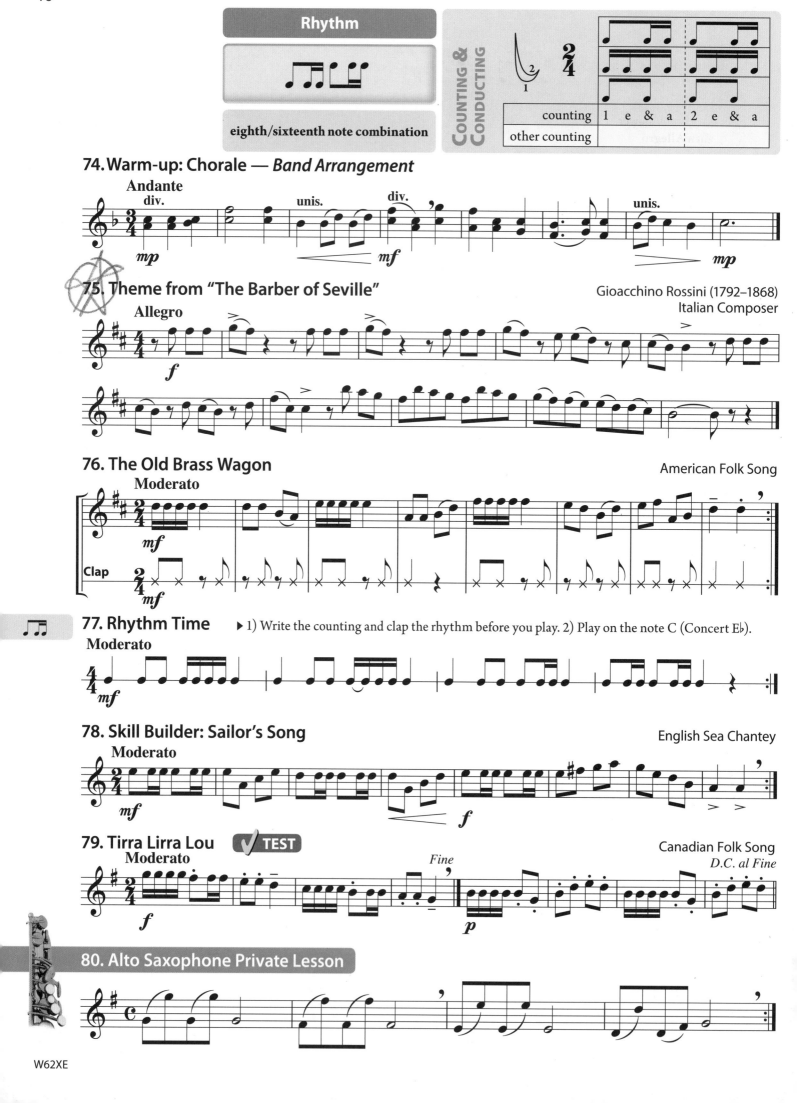

74. Warm-up: Chorale — *Band Arrangement*

Andante

75. Theme from "The Barber of Seville"

Gioacchino Rossini (1792–1868)
Italian Composer

Allegro

76. The Old Brass Wagon

American Folk Song

Moderato

Clap

77. Rhythm Time ▶ 1) Write the counting and clap the rhythm before you play. 2) Play on the note C (Concert E♭).

Moderato

78. Skill Builder: Sailor's Song

English Sea Chantey

Moderato

79. Tirra Lirra Lou ✓ **TEST**

Canadian Folk Song
D.C. al Fine

Moderato

Fine

80. Alto Saxophone Private Lesson

Terms & Symbols

Rhythm

Counting & Conducting

Allegretto – light and lively; slower than **Allegro**

sixteenth/eighth note combination

	counting	1	e	&	a	2	e	&	a
	other counting								

81. The Galway Piper

Irish Reel

Moderato

mf

82. Skill Builder

Moderato

mf

83. Rhythm Time

▸ 1) Write the counting and clap the rhythm before you play. 2) Play on the note D (Concert F).

Allegretto

mf

RHYTHM STUDIES: p. 45, #5, 11, 20

84. Sourwood Mountain

American Folk Song

Allegretto

mf

85. Big Rock Candy Mountain ✓ TEST

American Folk Song

Allegretto

mp   *mf*   *f*

86. Excellence in Composition

▸ Most of this composition is written already. 1) Complete this composition using notes and rhythms you know. 2) Add a tempo, dynamics, and slurs. 3) Play your composition. You might even come up with a title!

W62XE

Rhythm

dotted eighth/sixteenth note

Terms & Symbols

rallentando (*rall.*) – gradually slow the tempo

Counting & Conducting

	counting	1 e & a	2 e & a
	other counting		

Notes

B♭

alternate

87. Warm-up: Canon *(Round)*

Largo

Thomas Tallis was a composer for the royal courts of England's Henry VIII, Edward VI, Mary, and Elizabeth I from 1543–1585.

Thomas Tallis (c. 1505–1585)
English Composer

mp

88. Skill Builder: Theme from "Renaissance Festival and Dances"

Tielman Susato (c. 1500–c. 1562)
Flemish (Belgian) Composer
arr. Bruce Pearson

Moderato

Fine

mf – 1st time, *f* – 2nd & 3rd time

mp

D.C. al Fine

From *Renaissance Festival and Dances* (WB167), ©1995 Neil A. Kjos Music Company. Used with permission.

89. Rhythm Time

▶ 1) Write the counting and clap the rhythm before you play. 2) Play on the note C (Concert E♭).

mp

Rhythm Studies: p. 45, #6, 12, 21, 22

rallentando

90. O Tannenbaum

German Folk Song

Andante

rall.

mp

f

91. Blow Away the Morning Dew ~~Study~~ ✓ TEST

Allegretto

*Composer Ralph Vaughan-Williams used this tune in his **English Folk Song Suite**.*

English Folk Song

mf

f

rall. 2nd time

1.

2.

92. Alto Saxophone Private Lesson

▶ Use the alternate "one and one" fingering for B♭ on notes with ∗.

Mastering Excellence: p. 40, #4

Enharmonics

same sounding pitch written two different ways

Notes

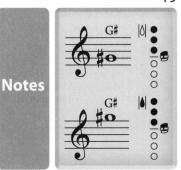

Terms & Symbols

coda – concluding section of a composition
Dal Segno al Coda (D.S. al Coda) – repeat the music starting from the sign (***segno***, 𝄋) and jump to the **coda** (⊕) where indicated

93. *Sight-Reading Challenge:* Procession of the Nobles

Nicolai Rimsky-Korsakov (1844–1908)
Russian Composer

enharmonics

94. Enharmonics

95. More Enharmonics

coda, D.S. al Coda

96. Skill Builder: Chromatic March

▶ Use the alternate fingering on notes with * .

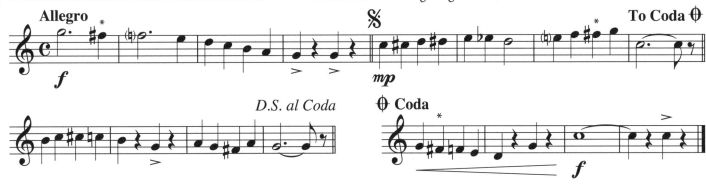

97. It's in the Bag ✓ TEST

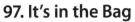

98. Excellence in Theory

▶ Write the enharmonic of the given pitch in both the staff and space provided. The first one has been done for you.

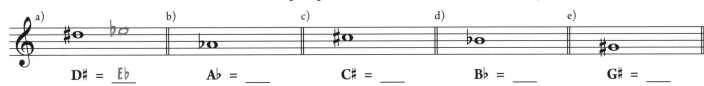

D♯ = E♭   **A♭** = ___   **C♯** = ___   **B♭** = ___   **G♯** = ___

W62XE

Solo

Hunting Song
Solo with Piano Accompaniment

Ryan Nowlin (b. 1978)
American Composer

Gregorian Chant and Ritual

Ryan Nowlin (b. 1978)
American Composer

Rain Dance

Dean Sorenson (b. 1963)
American Composer

W62XE

Enharmonics

Time Signature

𝄵   **cut time** or **alla breve**

𝄵 = **2/2**   = two counts per measure
= half note (𝅗𝅥) gets one count

Notes

Bb

alternate

Theory & Composition

chromatic scale – series of 12 ascending or descending half steps

COUNTING & CONDUCTING

	counting	1	&	2	&
	other counting				

99. Warm-up: Chorale — *Band Arrangement*
▶ Use the alternate fingering on the note with * .   Welsh Melody

Andante   *   *Fine*   *D.C. al Fine*

mp   *mf*   *f*

100. Skill Builder: Chromatic Scale
▶ Use the alternate fingering on notes with * .

chromatic scale

Andante   *   Gb *

mf

enharmonics

101. Rhythm Time
▶ 1) Write the counting and clap the rhythm before you play. 2) Play on the note C (Concert Eb).

𝄵

Moderato

mf

RHYTHM STUDIES: p. 46, #25-27

102. Yankee Doodle — *Duet*
American Folk Song

Moderato

A.

mf

B.

mf

103. High School Cadets March   ✓ TEST
▶ Use the alternate fingering on the note with * .

Sousa led "The President's Own" United States Marine Band under five presidents from 1880–1892.

John Philip Sousa (1854–1932) American Composer

Allegretto

mp   *mf*

1.   2.

f   *mp*

104. Alto Saxophone Private Lesson
▶ Use the alternate "one and one" fingering for Bb on notes with * .

MASTERING EXCELLENCE: p. 41, #5

Key Signature	Rhythm	Terms & Symbols

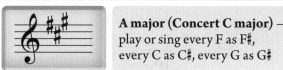
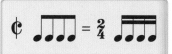

A major (Concert C major) – play or sing every F as F♯, every C as C♯, every G as G♯

licks or **riffs** – short melodic patterns associated with jazz music; used as material for improvisation

105. Skill Builder: Cindy

American Folk Song

106. A Major Scale, Arpeggio, and Chords (Concert C Major)

107. *Sight-Reading Challenge:* Suliram — *Duet* ▸ Circle the notes changed by the key signature.

Indonesian Folk Song

108. Rhythm Time ▸ 1) Write the counting and clap the rhythm before you play. 2) Play on the note A (Concert C).

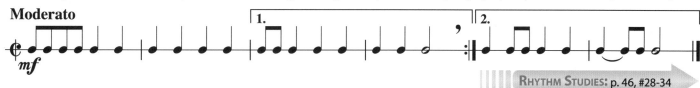

RHYTHM STUDIES: p. 46, #28-34

109. Dance Josey ✓TEST

American Folk Song

110. Excellence in Improvisation

▸ In the bars notated with slashes, improvise your own solo based on the G (Concert B♭) blues scale. Use new ideas or the licks you know while playing with the twelve-bar blues recorded accompaniment.

▸ Practice the following licks.

licks

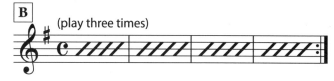

111. Warm-up — *Band Arrangement*

Andante

112. Anvil Chorus from "Il Trovatore"

This is one of the most famous choruses in all of the operatic repertoire of the Romantic Period.

Giuseppe Verdi (1813–1901)
Italian Composer

Maestoso

113. Skill Builder

Allegretto

114. Water Come a Me Eye — *Duet*

Jamaican music was heavily influenced by the music of other Caribbean countries, such as the calypso music of Trinidad and Tobago.

Jamaican Folk Song

Moderato

115. March of the Toreadors from "Carmen" ✓ TEST

Georges Bizet (1838–1875)
French Composer

Allegretto

116. Alto Saxophone Private Lesson

Rhythm

Time Signature

COUNTING & CONDUCTING

3 = three counts per measure
8 = eighth note (♪) gets one count

counting	1	2	3
other counting			

117. Skill Builder: The Stars and Stripes Forever

This is the National March of the U.S.A.

John Philip Sousa (1854–1932)
American Composer

Allegretto

118. Rhythm Time ▶ 1) Write the counting and clap the rhythm before you play. 2) Play on the note G (Concert B♭).
▶ Play **118. Rhythm Time** several times. Increase the tempo each time until you feel one beat per measure.

Allegro

RHYTHM STUDIES: p. 46, #35-40

119. Sea Chantey — *Duet* ▶ Play **119. Sea Chantey** several times. Start slowly, increasing the tempo each time until you feel one beat per measure.

American Sea Chantey

Allegro

A.

B.

120. The Merry Minstrels — *Round* ✓TEST

Henry Purcell was a singer and organist. He is called the father of English Baroque music.

Henry Purcell (1659–1695)
English Composer

Allegro (one primary beat per measure)

①

②

③

121. Excellence in Theory ▶ Rewrite the last four measures of **113. Skill Builder** in cut time (¢).
The first beat has been done for you.

Terms & Symbols

Adagio – slow tempo; faster than **Largo**

pp pianissimo – very soft

Time Signature

6 = six counts per measure
8 = eighth note (♪) gets one count

COUNTING & CONDUCTING

	counting	1	2	3	4	5	6
	other counting						

Notes

B♭

alternate

pp, Adagio

122. The Sea — *Duet*
Japanese Folk Song

Adagio *(3 beats per measure)*
div.

pp ——— *mp* ——— *pp* ——— *mp* ——— *pp*

6
8

123. Rhythm Time
▶ 1) Write the counting and clap the rhythm before you play. 2) Play on the note C (Concert E♭).
▶ Play **123. Rhythm Time** several times. Increase the tempo each time until you feel two beats per measure.

Allegro

mf

RHYTHM STUDIES: p. 46, #41-48

124. I'se the B'y that Builds the Boat
▶ Play several times. Increase the tempo each time until you feel two beats per measure.
Canadian Folk Song

Allegro

f

125. Skill Builder
▶ Use the alternate fingering on notes with ∗.

Moderato *(2 primary beats per measure)*

pp ——— *mf* ——— *pp* *mp* ——— *f* ——— *pp*

126. Lisbon Bay ✓TEST
*Composer Percy Grainger used this folk song in his famous work for band called **Lincolnshire Posy**.*
English Folk Song

Allegretto *(2 primary beats per measure)*

mf

1. *pp* **2.** *mf*

f *mf*

127. Alto Saxophone Private Lesson
▶ Use the "bis" key fingering for B♭ on notes with ∗.
▶ Keep your left hand index finger on the "bis" key on all notes requiring use of the first finger.

MASTERING EXCELLENCE: p. 41, #6

Key Signature — A minor (Concert C minor) – no sharps or flats

128. A Natural Minor Scale, Arpeggio, and Chords (Concert C Minor)

129. A Harmonic Minor Scale, Arpeggio, and Chords (Concert C Minor)

130. A Melodic Minor Scale, Arpeggio, and Chords (Concert C Minor)

131. Skill Builder: Habanera from "Carmen"

▶ Use the alternate fingerings on notes with *.

Georges Bizet (1838–1875)
French Composer

132. La Cumparsita ✓ TEST

The composer wrote this song when he was 19 years old. The title means "The Little Parade."

Gerardo H. Matos Rodríguez (1897–1948)
Uruguayan Composer

133. Excellence in Composition

▶ In the key of A minor (Concert C minor), write an original four-bar melody. You may use the natural, harmonic, or melodic minor scales. Be sure to include your clef, key signature, tempo, articulations, and dynamics. Two notes have been suggested. Give your composition a title and play it.

Title _____

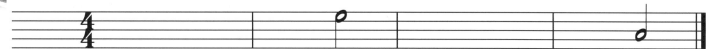

Terms & Symbols

cresc. – abbreviation for *crescendo*; gradually louder

dim. – abbreviation for *diminuendo*; gradually softer

Notes

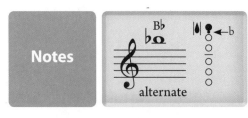

alternate

cresc., dim.

134. Warm-up: Evening Prayer from "Hansel and Gretel" — *Band Arrangement*

Engelbert Humperdinck (1854–1921)
German Composer

135. Skill Builder

136. *Sight-Reading Challenge:* La Donna è Mobile from "Rigoletto"

Giuseppe Verdi (1813–1901)
Italian Composer

137. When Johnny Comes Marching Home ✓ TEST

▶ Draw the bar lines before you play.

Patrick S. Gilmore (1829–1892)
American Composer

138. Alto Saxophone Private Lesson

▶ Use the "bis" key fingering for B♭ on notes with ∗.
▶ Keep your left hand index finger on the "bis" key on all notes requiring use of the first finger.

▐▌▌▌▌ **MASTERING EXCELLENCE:** p. 41, #7 ▶

Rhythm

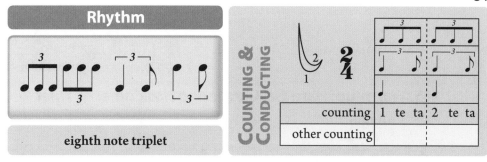

eighth note triplet

COUNTING & CONDUCTING

counting	1 te ta	2 te ta
other counting		

139. Little Donkey
▶ Name the key of **139. Little Donkey.** _____ Draw the bar lines before you play.   Chinese Folk Song

Moderato
mf

1.   2.

140. Rhythm Time
▶ 1) Write the counting and clap the rhythm before you play. 2) Play on the note A (Concert C).

Allegro
mf

RHYTHM STUDIES: p. 45, #23-24

141. Stars of the Heavens — *Duet*
Mexican Folk Song

Allegro
div.
f

142. Skill Builder

Moderato
mf

1.   2.

143. Triumphal March from "Aida"   ✓ TEST

Live elephants have appeared on stage during productions of this opera.

Giuseppe Verdi (1813–1901)
Italian Composer

Maestoso
f   *cresc.*   *ff*

144. Excellence in Improvisation

▶ Using pitches from the blues scale, improvise a melody. Play along with the twelve-bar blues recorded accompaniment.

A ▶ Play the G (Concert B♭) blues scale.

B   (play three times)

B minor (Concert D minor) – play or sing every F as F♯, every C as C♯

145. Warm-up: Haru Ga Kita *[Spring Has Come]* — *Duet*

Japanese Folk Song

146. B Natural Minor Scale, Arpeggio, and Chords (Concert D Minor)

147. B Harmonic Minor Scale, Arpeggio, and Chords (Concert D Minor)

148. B Melodic Minor Scale, Arpeggio, and Chords (Concert D Minor)

149. Skill Builder: Finale from Symphony No. 9 "From the New World"

Antonín Dvořák (1841–1904)
Czech Composer

150. Theme from "Tableau" ✔TEST ▶ Name the key of **150. Theme from "Tableau."** _____

Bruce Pearson (b. 1942)
American Composer

From *Tableau* (WB354), ©2006 Neil A. Kjos Music Company. Used with permission.

151. Alto Saxophone Private Lesson

MASTERING EXCELLENCE: p. 41, #8

152. Skill Builder

Moderato

153. The British Grenadiers

The origins of this march are in the 1600s. It soon became popular with armies all over Europe. Today, it is primarily associated with the regimental units of England.

English Folk Song

Allegretto

154. March from "The Nutcracker"

The Nutcracker ballet was premiered December 18, 1892, less than one year before the composer's death.

Peter Ilyich Tchaikovsky (1840–1893)
Russian Composer

Allegro

155. Follow the Drinkin' Gourd ✓ TEST

The "drinkin' gourd" is the Big Dipper constellation in the northern sky. By following these stars and traveling north, fleeing slaves could eventually reach freedom.

American Spiritual

Allegretto

BAND PIECES

| Terms & Symbols | **suite** – collection of short musical pieces unified by a common element |

Legends
(A Medieval Suite)

Ryan Nowlin (b. 1978)
American Composer

I. Once Upon a Time...

II. Trouble and Triumph

W62XE

III. The Return

Theory & Composition

strain – section of a composition, especially a march, containing a primary or secondary melody or theme
trio – third theme in a march, typically a contrasting section

The Washington Post March

John Philip Sousa
(1854–1932)
American Composer
arr. Ryan Nowlin

Bossa Caribe

Bruce Pearson (b. 1942)
American Composer
arr. Ryan Nowlin

W62XE

SOLO

Sonatina
from Sonatina in F Major, Op. 168, No. 1
Solo with Piano Accompaniment

Anton Diabelli (1781–1858)
Austrian Composer
arr. Bruce Pearson and Ryan Nowlin

W62XE

MASTERING EXCELLENCE

1. After page 2, #7

▶ Use the alternate fingering on notes with ∗ .

Basic Preparatory Exercise

Advanced Preparatory Exercise

Mastering Excellence

2. After page 8, #42

▶ Use the alternate fingering on notes with ∗ .

Basic Preparatory Exercise

Advanced Preparatory Exercise

Mastering Excellence

3. After page 12, #55

▶ Use the alternate fingering on notes with ∗ .

Basic Preparatory Exercise

Advanced Preparatory Exercise

Mastering Excellence

4. After page 18, #92

▶ Use the alternate "one and one" fingering for B♭ on notes with ∗ .

Basic Preparatory Exercise

Advanced Preparatory Exercise

Mastering Excellence

5. After page 24, #104

▸ Use the alternate "one and one" fingering for B♭ on notes with ∗ .

Basic Preparatory Exercise

Advanced Preparatory Exercise

Mastering Excellence

6. After page 28, #127

▸ Use the "bis" key fingering for B♭ on notes with ∗ .
▸ Keep your left hand index finger on the "bis" key on all notes requiring use of the first finger.

Basic Preparatory Exercise

Advanced Preparatory Exercise

Mastering Excellence

7. After page 30, #138

▸ Use the "bis" key fingering for B♭ on notes with ∗ .
▸ Keep your left hand index finger on the "bis" key on all notes requiring use of the first finger.

Basic Preparatory Exercise

Advanced Preparatory Exercise

Mastering Excellence

8. After page 32, #151

Basic Preparatory Exercise

Advanced Preparatory Exercise

Mastering Excellence

Chop Builders

A.

Andante

mf

B.

Andante

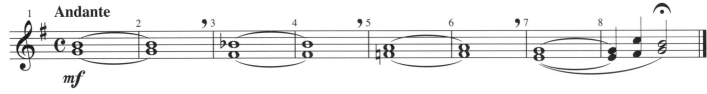

mf

Chromatic Scale

▶ Use the alternate fingering on notes with *.

▶ See p. 24, **100. Skill Builder: Chromatic Scale,** for a chromatic scale beginning on a different note.

G Major Warm-Up (Concert B♭ Major)

1. G Major Scale, Arpeggios, and Thirds

Major Scale   Arpeggios

Thirds

Melchior Teschner (1584–1635)
German Composer
arr. Bruce Pearson & Ryan Nowlin

2. G Major Chorale:
"All Glory, Laud, and Honor" — *Band Arrangement*

mf ——————— *f* ——— *mf* —— *mf* ————

——— *f* ——— *mf* ——— *f* ——— *mp*

▶ See p. 9, #43–45 for studies in the relative key, E minor (Concert G minor).

C Major Warm-Up (Concert E♭ Major)

▶ For notes you do not know, refer to the fingering chart.

1. C Major Scale, Arpeggios, and Thirds

2. C Major Chorale: "Crusader's Hymn" — *Band Arrangement*

Traditional
arr. Bruce Pearson & Ryan Nowlin

▶ See p. 29, #128–130 for studies in the relative key, A minor (Concert C minor).

D Major Warm-Up (Concert F Major)

1. D Major Scale, Arpeggios, and Thirds

2. D Major Chorale:
"Come, Thou Almighty King" — *Band Arrangement*

Felice de Giardini (1716–1796)
Italian Composer
arr. Bruce Pearson & Ryan Nowlin

▶ See p. 32, #146–148 for studies in the relative key, B minor (Concert D minor).

F Major Warm-Up (Concert A♭ Major)

1. F Major Scale, Arpeggios, and Thirds

2. F Major Chorale:
"For the Beauty of the Earth" — *Band Arrangement*

Conrad Kocher (1786–1872)
German Composer
arr. Bruce Pearson & Ryan Nowlin

A Major Warm-Up (Concert C Major)

1. A Major Scale, Arpeggios, and Thirds

Martin Luther (1483–1546)
German Composer
arr. Ryan Nowlin

2. A Major Chorale: "A Mighty Fortress" — *Band Arrangement*

RHYTHM STUDIES

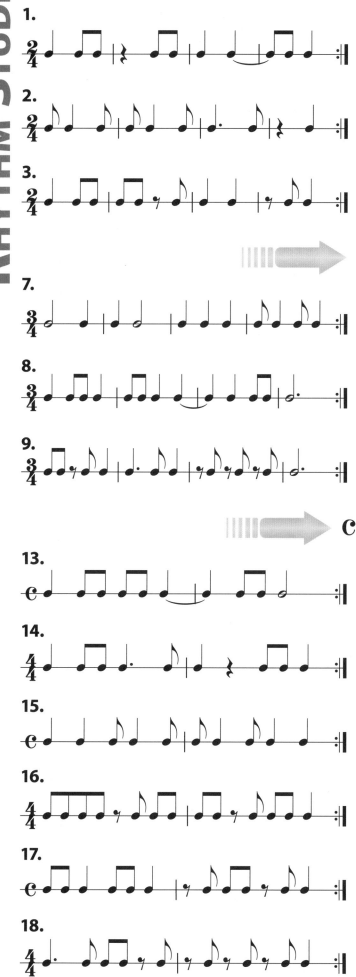

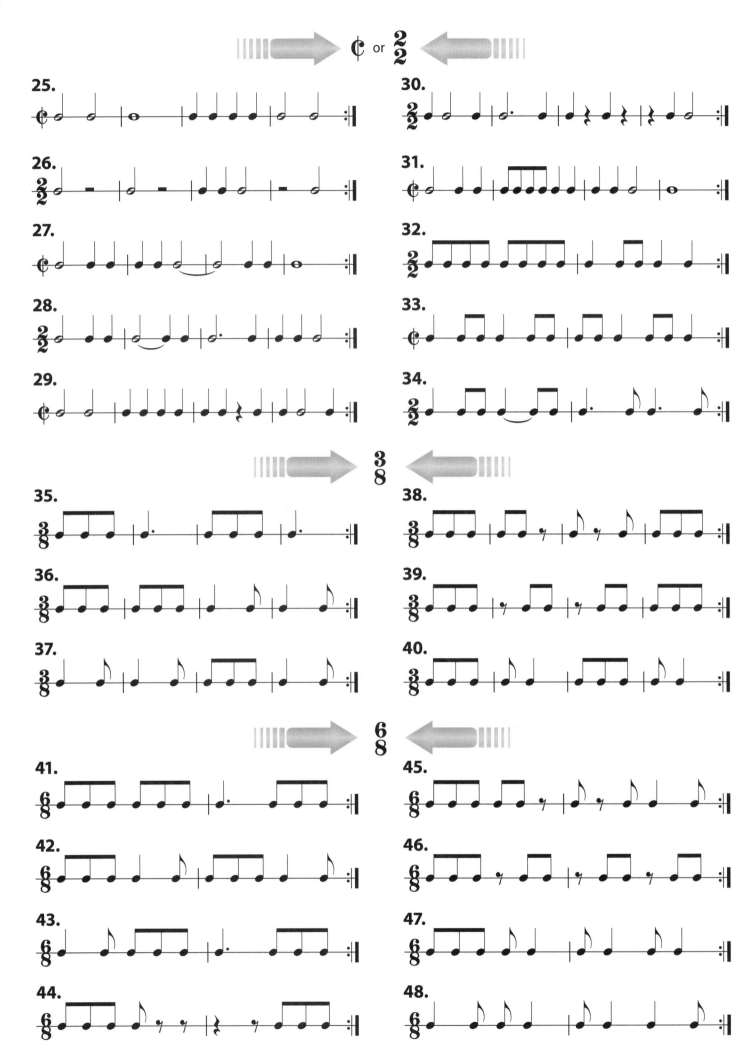

World Map

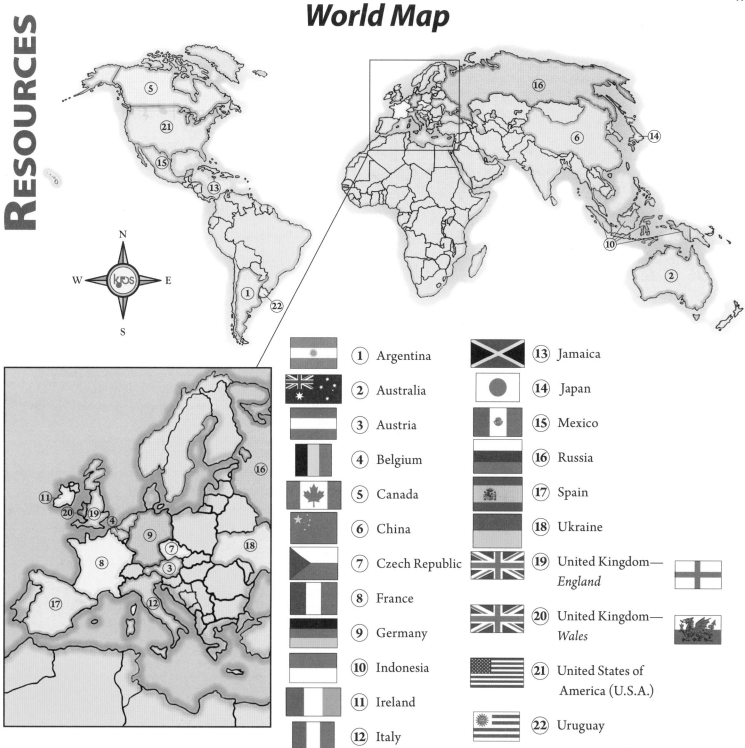

RESOURCES

1 Argentina	13 Jamaica
2 Australia	14 Japan
3 Austria	15 Mexico
4 Belgium	16 Russia
5 Canada	17 Spain
6 China	18 Ukraine
7 Czech Republic	19 United Kingdom—*England*
8 France	20 United Kingdom—*Wales*
9 Germany	21 United States of America (U.S.A.)
10 Indonesia	22 Uruguay
11 Ireland	
12 Italy	

Alto Saxophone Checklist

- ☐ Sitting up straight?
- ☐ Saxophone positioned on right side of body?
- ☐ Neck strap properly adjusted?
- ☐ Left and right thumbs correctly placed?
- ☐ Fingers gently curved?
- ☐ Wrists straight?
- ☐ Elbows away from body?
- ☐ Head erect?
- ☐ Mouthpiece proper distance in mouth?
- ☐ Top teeth resting directly on mouthpiece?
- ☐ Chin flat and pointed?
- ☐ Equal pressure on all sides of mouthpiece?
- ☐ Breathing correctly?
- ☐ Good tone produced?

Alto Saxophone Survival Kit

- ☐ swab
- ☐ soft, clean cloth
- ☐ neck strap
- ☐ extra reeds
- ☐ reed holder
- ☐ cork grease
- ☐ pencil
- ☐ method book
- ☐ band music
- ☐ music stand

Glossary/Index

Adagio – (p. 28) slow tempo; faster than **Largo**

alla breve – (p. 24) see **cut time**

Allegretto – (p. 17) light and lively; slower than **Allegro**

arpeggio – (p. 2) notes of a chord sounded one after another

binary form – (p. 10) music with two different sections

blues scale – (p. 13) series of whole (w) and half (h) steps in the following pattern: w+h, w, h, h, w+h, w; often used in jazz music

call and response – (p. 15) the call is a musical statement or question, and the response provides a musical answer

cautionary accidental – (p. 9) see **courtesy accidental**

chromatic scale – (p. 24) series of 12 ascending or descending half steps

coda – (p. 19) concluding section of a composition

courtesy accidental – (p. 9) reminder that the bar line has canceled an accidental

crescendo (cresc.) – (p. 30) gradually louder

cut time – (p. 24) a time signature indicating two counts per measure, the half note gets one count

Da Capo al Fine (D.C. al Fine) – (p. 5) go back to the beginning of the piece and play or sing until the *Fine*

Dal Segno al Coda (D.S. al Coda) – (p. 19) repeat the music starting from the sign (*segno*, 𝄋) and jump to the **coda** (⊕) where indicated

diminuendo (dim.) – (p. 30) gradually softer

dominant – (pp. 2, 9) fifth note of a scale; chord built on the fifth note of a scale

enharmonics – (pp. 19, 24) same sounding pitch written two different ways

fortissimo (ff) – (p. 26) very loud

harmonic minor scale – (p. 9) series of whole (w) and half (h) steps in the following pattern: w, h, w, w, h, w+h, h

interval – (p. 3) the distance between two pitches

Largo – (p. 5) very slow tempo

licks – (p. 25) short melodic patterns associated with jazz music; used as material for improvisation

Maestoso – (p. 6) majestically

major scale – (p. 2) series of whole (w) and half (h) steps in the following pattern: w, w, h, w, w, w, h

melodic minor scale – (p. 9) series of whole (w) and half (h) steps in the following pattern: (ascending) w, h, w, w, w, w, h; (descending) w, w, h, w, w, h, w

natural minor scale – (p. 9) series of whole (w) and half (h) steps in the following pattern: w, h, w, w, h, w, w

orchestration – (p. 2) choice of instruments used to play the music

pianissimo (pp) – (p. 28) very soft

rallentando (rall.) – (p. 18) gradually slow the tempo

riffs – (p. 25) see **licks**

ritardando (ritard. or rit.) – (p. 6) gradually slow the tempo

Roman numerals – (pp. 2, 9) used to indicate tonic, subdominant, and dominant chords

staccato – (p. 4) shorten the note

strain – (p. 36) section of a composition, especially a march, containing a primary or secondary melody or theme

subdominant – (pp. 2, 9) fourth note of a scale; chord built on the fourth note of a scale

suite – (p. 34) collection of short musical pieces unified by a common element

syncopation – (p. 7) rhythmic effect that places emphasis on a weak beat

tenuto – (p. 12) sustain a note for its full value

tonic – (pp. 2, 9) first note of a scale; chord built on the first note of a scale

transposition – (p. 7) taking a composition in one key and putting it in another

trio (march) – (p. 36) third theme in a march, typically a contrasting section

whole step – (p. 2) interval consisting of two half steps

Timeline

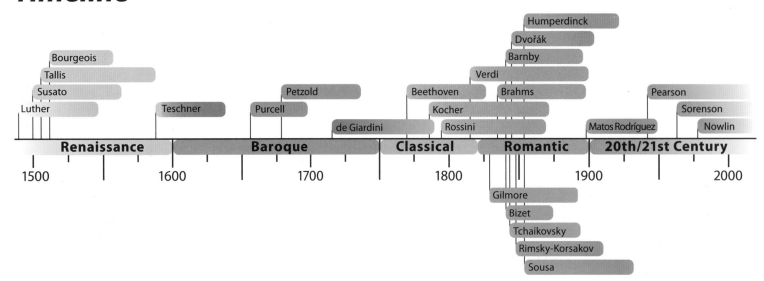